The Everyday Book

Jane Bull

The Everyday Book

Jane Bull

Design • Jane Bull
Text • Penelope Arlon
Photography • Andy Crawford
Design Assistance • Sadie Thomas

Publishing Manager • Sue Leonard
Managing Art Editor • Clare Shedden
Production • Shivani Pandey
DTP Designer • Almudena Díaz

For Charlotte, Billy, and James

This edition first published in 2006 by
Dorling Kindersley Limited.
Exclusively for Marks and Spencer p.l.c.

www.marksandspencer.com

Printed and bound in China.

ISBN 1-4053-1488-5

The everyday book of things to make and do

"I'm bored, what can I do?"
How often do you find yourself
thinking this?
Well here's how to answer the
"I'm bored" question – a whole
book of things to make and do
whatever the weather!

If it's pouring with rain try the
scrap bags, the string things, or
a spot of baking, and if the
weather is fine, set up camp and
serve sunny fruit cocktails. The
most important thing to do is
get creative, use your
imaginations, and

have fun!

In this everyday book you'll find...

hundreds of reasons...

to get crafty!

It's filled with bright ideas

so weave away boredom...

and have some fun!

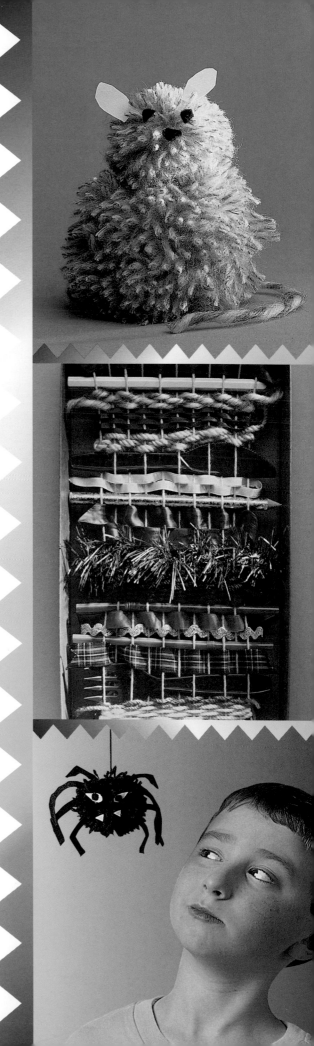

Rainy day survival kit

Be prepared – Collect bits and pieces regularly, such as all these things around the page, so that when it rains, you have lots to work with.

Look for Bob on this page
Find out who he is on page 48

Materials and tools used in the book

Felt pens • Plain paper • Face paints and sponges
• Paint brushes • Wallpaper paste • Glue
• Scraps of material • Knitting and sewing needles
• Scissors • String • Wool • All kinds of paper
• Buttons and beads • Materials to cook with

How to Survive a
Rainy Day

The rain is pouring down and there's simply nowhere to go. What are you going to do? You could watch television OR you could have some fun.

Why not feast on cookies, take a dot for a walk, say "hello" to your hands, get wrapped up in string, and if it's still raining after all that, you can try catching it!

Rainy day doodles

You won't believe what you can do with a doodle! Just put the pen down on the page and wave and wriggle away.
Let your pen run free!

Take a dot for a walk

and colour in the spaces

Lines and loops

It may look complicated but that's the beauty of it. It's easy!
Draw straight lines across the paper, then draw a loopy
shape over the top. Now colour in alternate shapes.

Take a dot for another walk

Put your pen down and let your hand move freely across
a page. Feel free to cross lines and cut up circles. Now
colour in each shape and watch the pattern come to life.

Eye-boggling spiral

Draw lots of circles from the centre, each getting bigger,
then draw lines outwards, like a web. Colour them in.

weaving waves

Draw wavy lines across the page and down. Then
colour in alternate squares for bulging patterns.

Hello hands!

Face paints

Forget your face, paint your hands instead! Turn your fingers into little personalities.

Water for thinning paint.

Fine and thick brushes, and a washable felt pen.

Sponges to paint large areas.

wet the sponge, and dab it in the paint.

Paint your hand all over with the sponge.

Add the details with a paint brush.

Football crazy

Lets go!

My ball

Yes!

I liked the sliding tackle. Good game Jim!

Hints and tips

- Choose a good quality face paint.
- Look at your hands and decide on a shape that suits your fingers.
- Use a damp sponge to cover large areas. Wait for it to dry before you paint the details.
- Use a washable felt pen for outlines and faces.
- Clean the paints off with soap and water.

Pretty Polly

Creatures with beaks and long necks work well too, like this parrot. Try other birds – a cockerel or a pink flamingo.

Elephant fingers

I am an alien

paper pots

There's paper all around you. Don't throw it away, recycle it!

Sweet wrappers

Coloured foil

Envelopes

Coloured paper

Comics

Magazines

Newspaper

How to make a pot

Vaseline

1. Blow up a balloon, spread vaseline over it, brush over some paste, and half cover it with paper.

See page 46 for more about paste.

Wallpaper paste

2. Cover the balloon with about six layers. Leave it to dry in a warm place.

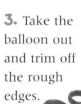

3. Take the balloon out and trim off the rough edges.

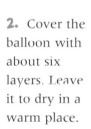

4. Make a base with a strip of card, tape it on, and cover it with paste and paper.

5. Cut card for ears, tape in place, and again cover with paste and paper.

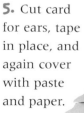

Decorate inside and out.

Box rooms

where your toys can live. Decorate and furnish them with bits and bobs

Find a cardboard box

Measure up the paper

Use wrapping paper or paint your own wallpaper.

Draw and cut out windows

you will need

For the house itself:
- A cardboard box
- Scissors, ruler, and pen
- Decorated wallpaper
- Material for the carpet
- Glue

Decorate the walls

Glue the wallpaper to the inside of the box.

☆ **Ask an Adult** to help cut the thick card.

Cover the floor

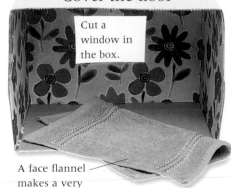

Cut a window in the box.

A face flannel makes a very good carpet.

Ahh, home sweet home

Come in out of the rain

All I need now is a comfy chair

How to make scrap furniture

Collect boxes, cartons, and other bits and pieces that are going to be thrown away – imagine how many you will gather over the weeks for those rainy days. You'll have a great collection.

Small boxes

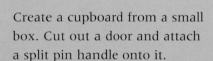

Create a cupboard from a small box. Cut out a door and attach a split pin handle onto it.

Lamp

Stick a straw in a cotton reel and pop a paper cake case on top.

Lollypop sticks

Icecream cone

Armchair

Paint four matchboxes and glue them together.

Clothes peg

Matchboxes

Bottle lid

Table

Stick a large lid onto a drinks bottle lid with a piece of modelling clay.

Modelling clay

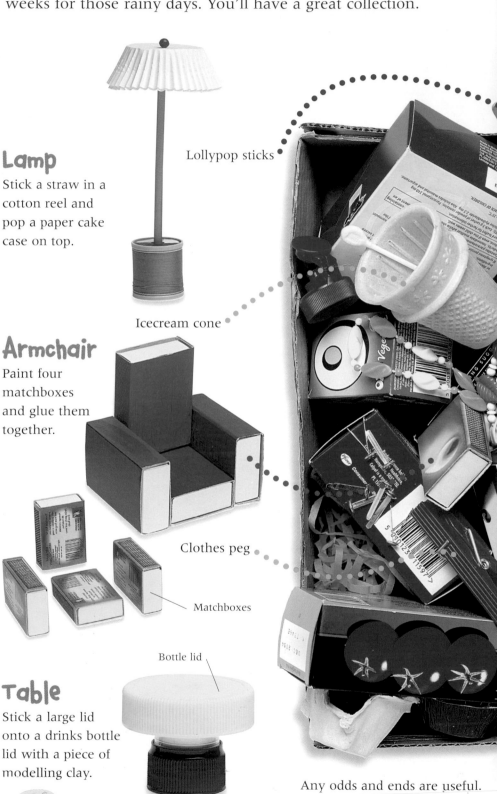

Any odds and ends are useful. Use your imagination to think of other bits of furniture that can go inside your box room.

You will need

- Odds and ends from around the house.
- Sticky tape
- Paper fasteners
- Paint and brushes
- Modelling clay
- Split pins
- Glue

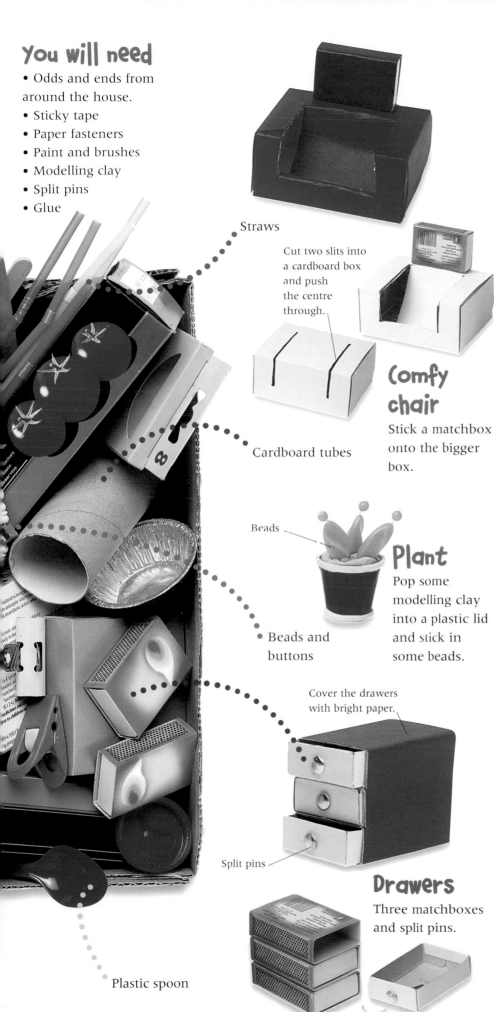

Straws

Cut two slits into a cardboard box and push the centre through.

Comfy chair

Cardboard tubes

Stick a matchbox onto the bigger box.

Beads

Plant

Pop some modelling clay into a plastic lid and stick in some beads.

Beads and buttons

Cover the drawers with bright paper.

Split pins

Drawers

Three matchboxes and split pins.

Plastic spoon

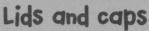

Lids and caps

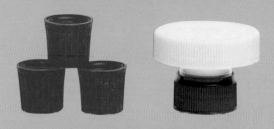

Lids from empty tubes of paint make tiny beakers or plant pots. Lids and caps can be made into tiny tables.

Pets corner

Create cages for your furry toys

– open your very own animal hospital.

You will need

- Cardboard box
- Glue, tape
- Scissors
- Split pins
- Black pen

Cosy hutch

Help your cuddly pets feel right at home by cutting strips of scrap paper for their bed. Give them bowls for food and water and every so often let them out for a cuddle. The good thing about toy pets is that they never need cleaning out!

Draw swirls on the cardboard with a black pen to make it look like wood.

Cage door

Make a cage door for your hutch with strips of card. Measure your box and cut two long pieces of card and two shorter pieces.

The long pieces must be about 6 cm (2 in) longer than the length of the box.

Attach the strips together with split pins,

Make sure that it fits exactly onto the outside of the box.

It's feeding time!

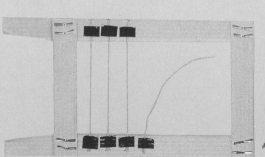

Use wool as your caged bars by sticking lengths to the top and bottom of the back.

Attach the cage door by gluing the flaps to the side of the box. Alternatively you could use split pins.

Make a latch out of card and a split pin.

Salt dough

Four activities in one

1. Mixing
2. Modelling
3. Cooking
4. Painting

Mix the dough and squeeze it into any shape you like. Hours of doughy fun.

To make the dough

You will need

water
200 ml
(1/3 pint)

Salt
300 g (10 oz)

Flour
300 g
(10 oz)

Oil
2 tsp

Put all of the ingredients into a bowl.

Squeeze the mixture together.

Pat it into a ball.

Roll it out

Now have a play!

Play with your dough

Roll it, rake it, squash it, squeeze it. Look around your house for objects to press into the dough. You can create all sorts of effects and shapes and if you don't like them, roll it up and start again.

If the dough gets sticky, sprinkle on some flour.

Bear necessities

Make the

Squash a
paperclip
onto the
back.

Stick them
together.

Bake the
bear then
paint it.

Tie on
some
string.

Baking your shapes

Place your shapes on a baking tray.

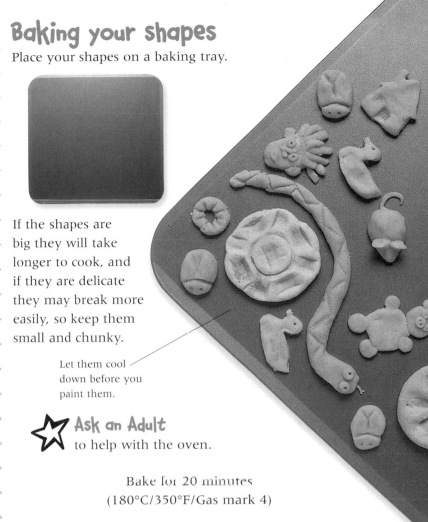

If the shapes are
big they will take
longer to cook, and
if they are delicate
they may break more
easily, so keep them
small and chunky.

Let them cool
down before you
paint them.

⭐ **Ask an Adult**
to help with the oven.

Bake for 20 minutes
(180°C/350°F/Gas mark 4)

Painting and decorating

When the baked dough has
cooled down, you can paint
it with poster or acrylic
paint. Try mixing a
little PVA glue with
the paint (about 1
part PVA to 2 parts
paint), this will make
it tough and shiny.

More about
PVA glue
on page 46.

Keeping your dough

You can save your
unbaked dough by
covering it in
plastic wrap. It
will keep for
about two weeks.

Save it for a rainy day

25

Sweet dough

Dough you can eat - make these tasty shortbread biscuits.

Flour

Butter

Sugar

Yum Yum

Roll the dough into a ball and squash it flat.

Squash with a fork

Biscuit Mix

Makes 12-16
Plain biscuits
300 g (6 oz) plain flour
200 g (4 oz) butter
100 g (2 oz) sugar

Put the flour, sugar, and butter into a bowl.
Squeeze them together with your fingers until they come together to make a ball of dough.
Shape your biscuits and decorate them.
Place them on a baking tray.
Cook for 15 minutes (160°C/325°F/Gas mark 3)
Cool them on a cooling rack and TUCK IN!

For chocolate biscuits:
250 g (5 oz) plain flour
50 g (2 oz) cocoa powder
100 g (4 oz) butter
50 g (2 oz) sugar

For coconut biscuits:
Add 50 g (2 oz) coconut to to mix.

 Ask an Adult to help with the oven.

Leave some space between your biscuits.

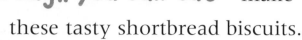

Making patterns

Try sugar strands and colourful sweets for decoration, or use plain and chocolate dough together to create spots and stripes.

Sugar strands

Choc drops

Choc sweets

Big chocolate sweets

use the furniture

It will give extra height to the chutes.

Grrrr!

all set for the Domino Run? Go!

A spectacular run

Push the car at the top of the stool and watch it go! Set up the dominoes so that as one falls, it will knock down the next and so on. The aim is to create a set that will fall from beginning to end without stopping.

You will need

- Dominoes
- Boxes
- Cardboard tubes
- Building bricks
- Bits and pieces to help the run.

what will happen? Turn to page 46

Get weaving

Wonderful webs in rainbow colours.

Paper plate

wool

A paper plate and scraps of wool create a rainbow web to brighten up your day.

To weave a web
You will need
- A paper plate or a circle of card
- Scraps of wool
- Darning needle

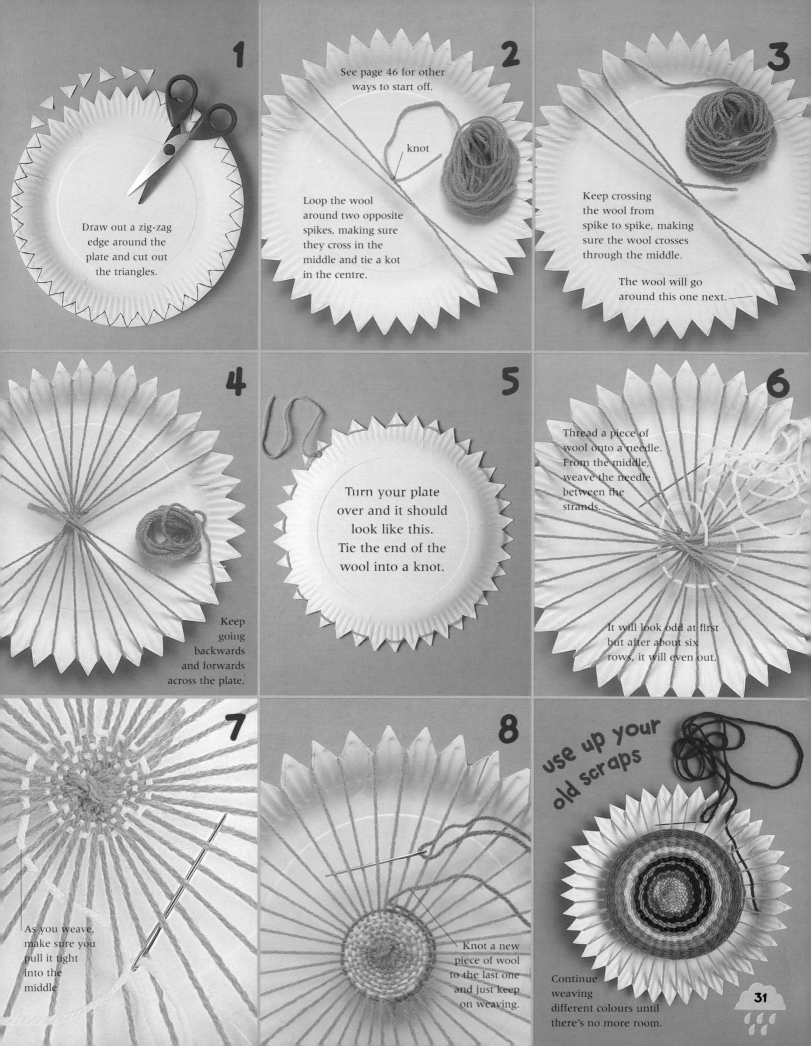

1

Draw out a zig-zag edge around the plate and cut out the triangles.

2

See page 46 for other ways to start off.

knot

Loop the wool around two opposite spikes, making sure they cross in the middle and tie a kot in the centre.

3

Keep crossing the wool from spike to spike, making sure the wool crosses through the middle.

The wool will go around this one next.

4

Keep going backwards and forwards across the plate.

5

Turn your plate over and it should look like this. Tie the end of the wool into a knot.

6

Thread a piece of wool onto a needle. From the middle, weave the needle between the strands.

It will look odd at first but after about six rows, it will even out.

7

As you weave, make sure you pull it tight into the middle

8

Knot a new piece of wool to the last one and just keep on weaving.

use up your old scraps

Continue weaving different colours until there's no more room.

31

keep on weaving

Looms are frames used for weaving fabric. Make a simple loom and have a go at creating a piece of fabric and then start to weave anything you can find!

Home-made loom

A shoebox lid is ideal. Cut the same number of slits on opposite ends then thread wool backwards and forwards.

1

 Ask an Adult to cut the slits, they may need to use a sharp knife.

2

Wrap the wool around the first slit to hold it in place.

3

Keep going up and down.

4

Thread the wool above and below the main strands and forward and back.

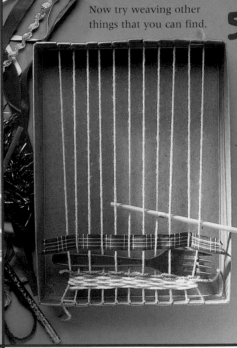

5

Now try weaving other things that you can find.

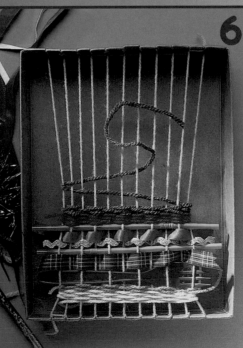

6

Weave and weave until you reach the top.

A work of weaving art – attach it to the wall for all to see.

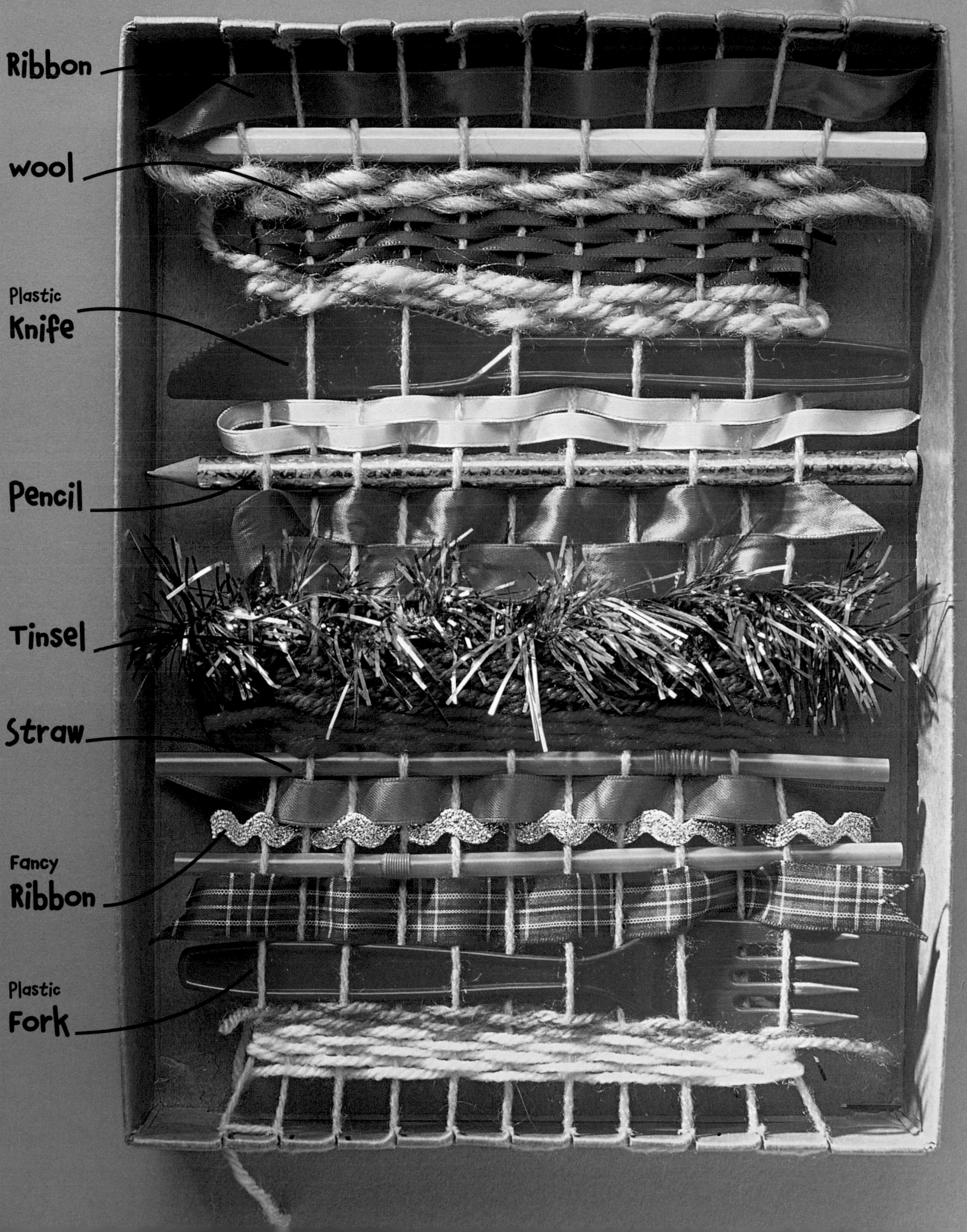

Ribbon

wool

Plastic **Knife**

Pencil

Tinsel

Straw

Fancy **Ribbon**

Plastic **Fork**

Scrap bags

These floppy bag people are made from scraps of left-over material and filled with dried beans.

"Try me I'm very filling", yell the lentils.

Play with us, we're full of beans!

35

Throw together a scrap bag

Here, catch!

To make a bag

Use the scrap bag pattern to measure the size of your bag. Cut out a piece of fabric and fold it in half.

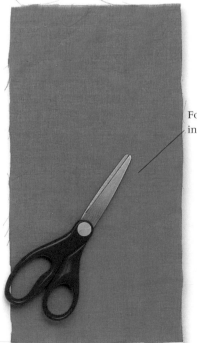

Fold it in half.

Scrap bag pattern

Follow this

pattern to help

you with the size.

LEAVE A HOLE

STITCHING LINE

FOLD THE FABRIC HERE

STITCHING LINE

LEAVE A HOLE

Leave an opening
at the top.

Back stitch around
the open sides.

Turn the bag
inside out.

Fill it up with
lentil beans.

To finish it off,
stitch up the hole
at the top.

Pin it together

Sew up the sides

Turn inside out and fill up

Close it up

Back stitch

A good stitch to use is back stitch because it completely seals the sides. Don't be fooled into thinking you can do a simple running stitch, if you do the beans will fall out!

See page 50 for back stitch instructions.

Sew or use PVA glue to attach the faces.

Scrap bag games

Target practice

Set up a target area around a bucket and challenge your family to score high. Make up the rules yourself!

Juggling

Start with two then build up your bags. A perfect practice for a rainy day.

Play catch

Throw a bag for a friend to catch. If they miss they go down on one knee, miss again they go down on two knees, and so on until they are lying down.

Bad luck! To score 100 it must go right into the bowl.

100

50

25

Good shot, that's 100 points!

string things

what a wind up! See-through string balls and fluffy pom-poms, there's a whole new woolly world to discover.

Juggle those pom-poms!

How to make a string thing

You will need • Balloon • String or wool • Wallpaper paste • Vaseline

Blow up a balloon and spread Vaseline all over it – this will stop the string sticking to the balloon.

Mix up a bowl of wallpaper paste.

Cut some lengths of string, about 60 cm (22 in) long.

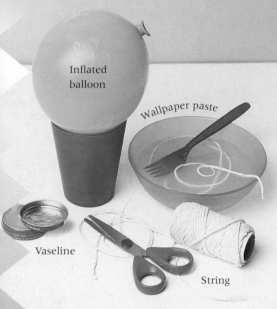

Inflated balloon

Wallpaper paste

Vaseline

String

Dip the string into the paste, then wrap it around the balloon.

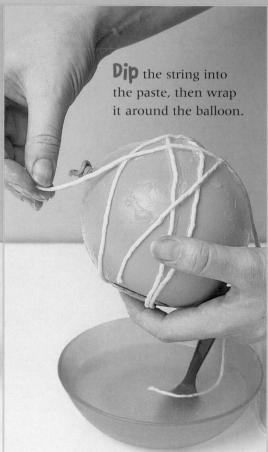

Watch out!
This bit gets messy

Add More and more and more string until you have enough.

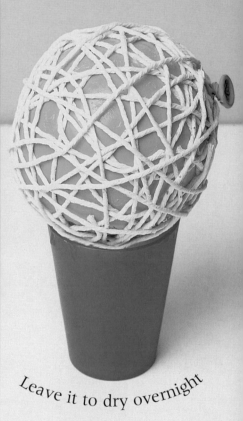

Leave it to dry overnight

How to make a Pom-pom

You will need • Thin card • Wool

Tip: The larger the discs, the bigger your pom-pom will turn out.

Knot the wool in place.

10 cm (4 in)

Add more wool until it's completely covered.

Cut two discs from thin card.

Cut a 3 cm (1¹/5 in) diameter hole in the middle.

Put the two discs of card together.

Wind the wool around and around – through the middle and over the top.

When the string is dry...

pop the balloon!

Put the scissors between the two discs.

Tip For multi-colours add different wool as you wind.

Snip away any long bits.

Snip the wool all the way around.

Hold it firmly in the middle.

Open up the discs slightly.

Tie a piece of wool tightly around the middle.

Pull the card off and fluff up the wool.

A pom-pom – it's magic!

why not make a friendship bracelet for your favourite friend?

Knitting

Master the skill of knitting. Begin with your fingers and thumbs and work up to needles. As well as wool, you will need lots of patience, so DON'T give up.

Finger knitting

This is also called finger crochet. Wind the wool around your thumb twice then pick up the first loop and take it over the second. Keep repeating this until it has grown to the length you want.

It's growing

As you repeat the steps, the bracelet will grow and grow.

1 Wind the wool around your thumb twice.

2 Pick up the first loop.

3 Take it over the second loop.

4 Keep going.

5 Carefully pull the wool.

6 Pull the wool so the stitch is secure on your finger.

7 Repeat the steps. The first loop is there, so wind the wool to make the second.

Use two pieces of different coloured wool to make a multicoloured wristband.

Knit a blanket

Once you have got the hang of
finger knitting, you will have a
good idea how to cast on to
needles and start knitting. Using
plain stitch you can make a finger
puppet from a single square, and
if you get really ambitious you
can make lots of squares
to make a blanket.

I'm in stitches!

How to knit

Follow these knitting instructions and you'll be using plain stitch with standard needles. Once you have got the hang of it there will be no stopping you – you'll be well and truly hooked!

You will need
- Knitting needles size 4 mm (no.9)
- Ball of wool

Casting on – this is how you get the stitches onto the needle.

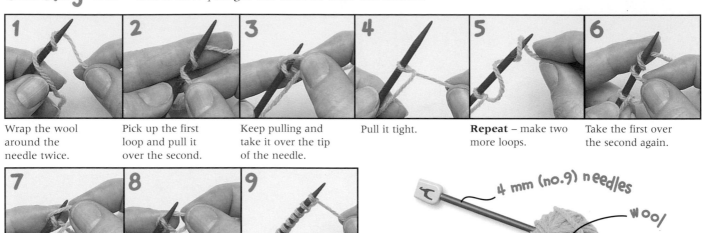

1 Wrap the wool around the needle twice.

2 Pick up the first loop and pull it over the second.

3 Keep pulling and take it over the tip of the needle.

4 Pull it tight.

5 **Repeat** – make two more loops.

6 Take the first over the second again.

7 Keep pulling it tight as you go.

8 Take it right over the needle again, as before.

9 Keep repeating this until you have 12 stitches.

4 mm (no.9) needles

wool

Plain stitch

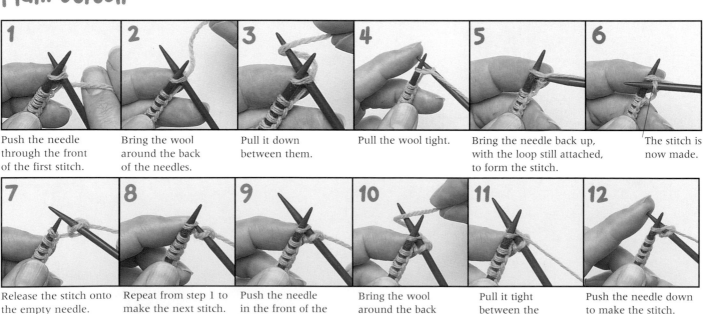

1 Push the needle through the front of the first stitch.

2 Bring the wool around the back of the needles.

3 Pull it down between them.

4 Pull the wool tight.

5 Bring the needle back up, with the loop still attached, to form the stitch.

6 The stitch is now made.

7 Release the stitch onto the empty needle.

8 Repeat from step 1 to make the next stitch.

9 Push the needle in the front of the next stitch.

10 Bring the wool around the back of the needles.

11 Pull it tight between the needles.

12 Push the needle down to make the stitch.

13 Bring the needle back and to the front again.

14 You now have two stitches.

15 Keep doing this until you finish the row.

The second stitch is now made.

Keep Going!

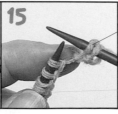

Repeat these steps until you reach the length you want.

Casting off – do this when you have reached the length you want.

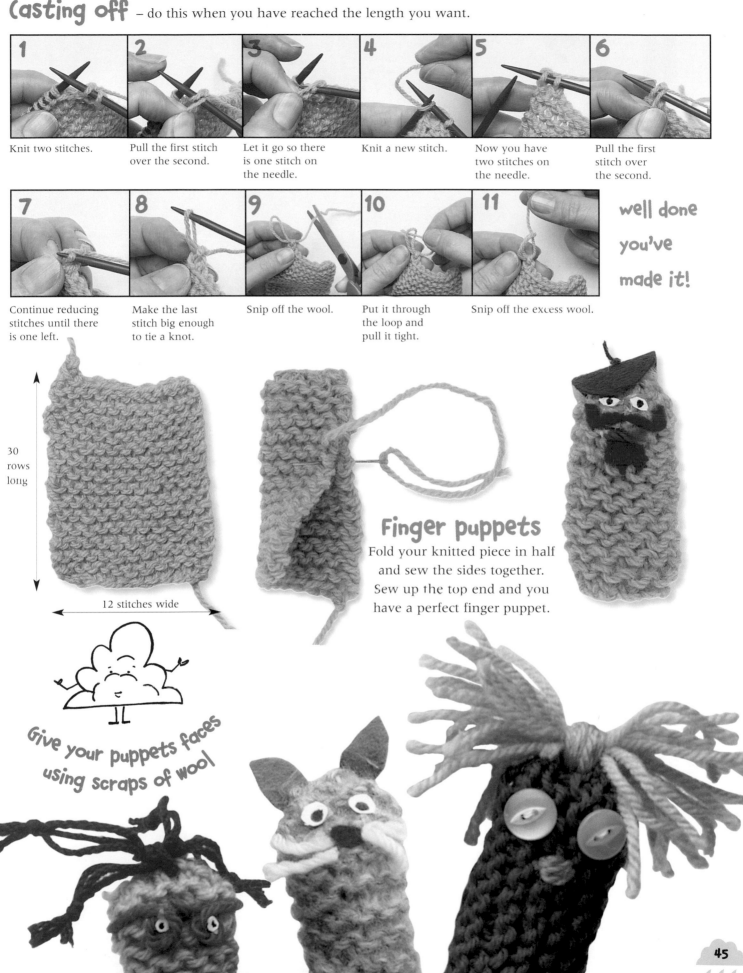

1 Knit two stitches.

2 Pull the first stitch over the second.

3 Let it go so there is one stitch on the needle.

4 Knit a new stitch.

5 Now you have two stitches on the needle.

6 Pull the first stitch over the second.

7 Continue reducing stitches until there is one left.

8 Make the last stitch big enough to tie a knot.

9 Snip off the wool.

10 Put it through the loop and pull it tight.

11 Snip off the excess wool.

well done you've made it!

30 rows long

12 stitches wide

Finger puppets

Fold your knitted piece in half and sew the sides together. Sew up the top end and you have a perfect finger puppet.

Give your puppets faces using scraps of wool

45

The Domino effect

Now it's time to see what happens when you knock the first little car down the ramp. Watch out!

Tunnels and ramps can be made from cardboard tubes, either cut in half or whole.

Domino tip

Be very, very careful when you lay the dominoes out. If you make a mistake, you may have to start again.

It's a complete mess!

It doesn't stop!

Away it goes!

The car hits the dominoes, the dominoes ram the car, and whoosh! It flies through the tunnel, straight into the people standing at the bottom!

Down the tube

ar....yum yum!

Chain reaction

Everything is all over the place, as one goes the others follow. What a mess and what a noise!

Crash and its over!

The grand finale

The dominoes crash into the truck, which rolls down the ramp, knocks into the tube carrying the strainer full of sweets, which falls and the dinosaur gets his meal. Phew!

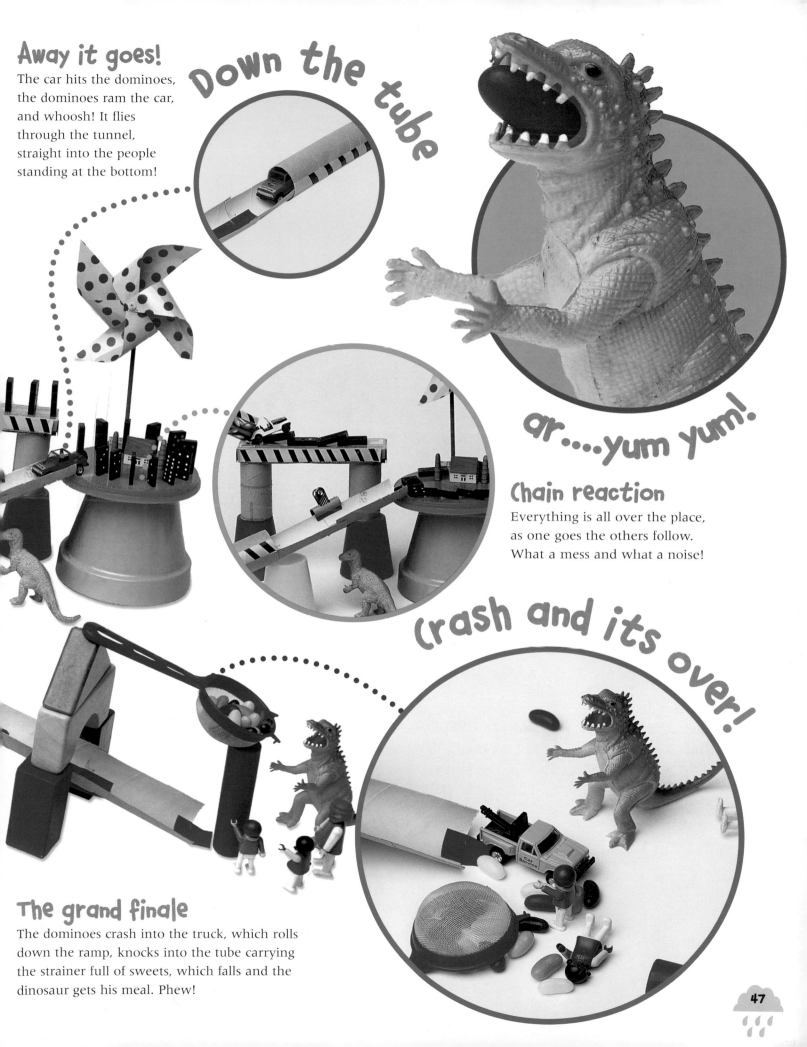

Activity centres – jars packed full of fun

Jars are perfect for filling with lots of little things for your craft projects. Alternatively, fill one up with games, such as dice and cards – useful for those rainy days.

Cards, counters, and quizzes

Beads, buttons, and ribbons

Where's Bob?

A game of hide and seek If you look carefully throughout this book, you will see Bob popping up on certain spreads. Have you seen him yet? The pages he is on are listed on page 96.

Come and get me!

Memory game

Look at these objects for 30 seconds. Now close the book and see how many you can remember. How did you score?

How many can you remember?

Try this on your family. Prepare a tray of objects. Let them study it for 30 seconds. **Time's up!** Quickly cover it with a cloth and the one who can remember all the objects is the winner!

Take a **potato** and make...

Potato heads

Use buttons, cocktail sticks, hairclips, faces from magazines, or anything else you can think of to dress up your potatoes.

Pin the faces in place.

A potato pooch

Potato bake

Scrub and wash a potato. Put it straight in the oven set at 190°C/375°F/Gas mark 5. Bake for about an hour, or until it's soft inside. Take it out and fill it up with cheese.

Cheese and chives on the top.

Potato patterns

Cut a potato in half and draw a shape on the inside with felt pen. Carefully cut it out with a knife – remember to cut around your design. Brush paint onto the surface and press it onto some paper.

Don't put on too much paint.

Keep designs simple

49

All about glue

Glue stick   Wallpaper paste   All-purpose glue

wallpaper paste

You can buy this paste in bags from any hardware shop. Put about a tablespoon of the flakes into a bowl and add water until it blends in. It should be thick enough to brush onto a surface.

Glue stick

This is a very clean glue and is best for paper as it won't make it crinkle.

All-purpose glue

This is not only a strong glue, it also smells strong too. Use it for gluing cardboard pieces together.

PVA glue

PVA is very useful glue that works on fabric and card. Mixed with a bit of water it is a good varnish, and mixed with paint, it will give the coloured surface a shiny finish.

Threading a needle

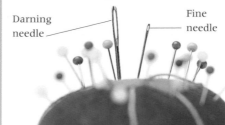

Darning needle   Fine needle

Push the fine wire through the eye.

This gadget helps you thread a needle, You can get them anywhere that sells cotton.

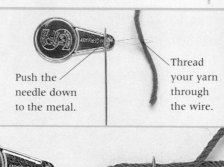

Push the needle down to the metal.

Thread your yarn through the wire.

Now just pull the threader and the needle apart and you've done it - easy!

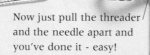

Carry on pulling and then removed the wire threader.

Sewing backstich

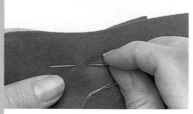

Knot the end of the cotton and push the needle down and up through the fabric

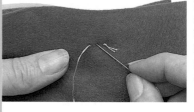

Pull the needle all the way through t the knot.

Place the needle between t knot and the dangli cotton.

Bring the needle up ahead of t dangling cotton.

Repeat the steps and sew over a few stitche to finish o

Get weaving
(page 30)

Quick start and finish

If you have trouble getting your weaving started, use sticky tape to hold the wool in place.

Tape the wool to the back of the plate.

Turn the plate over and wind the wool.

When you have finished turn the plate over.

How to make a rain catcher

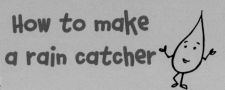

Take a plastic bottle – one with a flat bottom is the best.

Ask an Adult to help you cut the bottle.

Cut the bottle into two pieces as shown.

Turn the top over and place it back into the bottle base.

Make a dip stick from a wooden spoon. Measure and draw out 1 cm (1/2 in) spaces with a pen.

Pop a drop of food colouring into the bottle so that you can see the water easily.

Rain catcher

Rain, rain, go away

If the rain won't go away, make yourself a gauge to measure just how much has fallen. Place some pebbles around the bottom to keep it stable, and check the depth each day against the dip stick.

Sunny time

Track the sun as it moves
across the sky, and keep track of time.

Is it time for a drink?

8
9
10
11
midday **12**
1
2
3
4
5
6
7

Sundials

As the sun moves across the sky, believe it or not it can tell you the time. Stand something tall, such as a stick, in a bucket of sand in an area that gets sunlight all day. Each hour place a shell where the shadow of the stick falls and note down what time it is. The next day you can tell the time by using it!

Fun times in the sun

All you need is a bright sunny day and some things to mark the hours as they pass. If you are on a beach use shells – and turn over to learn how to make a sundial for your garden.

midday
12
11   1
10   2
9   3
8   4
      5
      6
      7

Make a clock wherever you are.

Check your clock time after time

Making time

Try putting the shells on the tip of the stick shadow and at the end of the day see what shape you have made. It might not quite be circular like a watch. That's weird! If you make the sundial out of pebbles or shells then you can leave it out all year round. Does it work at all times of the year?

53

Sun clock

Time to watch the clock in the garden.

what's the time?

Impress your friends by being able to tell the time without looking at a watch. How do you do it? By using the sun.

54

How to make a clock

You will need:

- Paper plate
- Terracotta plant pot
- Stick or garden cane
- A watch
- Strips of paper
- Sticky tack

Before you assemble your sun clock, decorate the plate, stick, and pot.

1. Make a hole in the centre of the plate and push the cane through.

Put sticky tack around the hole.

2. Now put the cane through the hole in the plant pot.

Press the plate onto the sticky tack.

3. Make sure the plate doesn't turn easily on the stick.

use the sunlight to set your clock

You will need a whole sunny day to set your clock so that you can read it the next day.

1. Place your clock in a sunny area.

2. The stick will cast a shadow across the plate. This is the sun telling you the time.

3. Now look at your watch, and mark the shadow on each hour with a strip of paper. For example at 10 o'clock mark the shadow, then continue until the sun goes down.

4. The next day, tell the time by seeing where the shadow falls!

10 o'clock   12 o'clock   2 o'clock

Midday 12

It's just past 3 o'clock

11 12 1 2 3 4 5 6 7 8 9 10

Make the 12 o'clock strip look different to remind you where it is.

55

Take cover

Stay out of the sun in a home-made hide-away.

Keep the enemy away!

No entry unless you know the password

keep out

Beware!

When the sun is getting too hot and you need some shade, don't go indoors – build a tent in the garden with some blankets and garden canes.

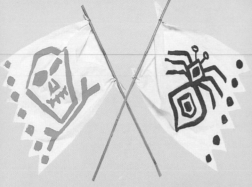

Picnic pots

Setting up camp

Once you've made your camp, you will need food supplies. Hang clear notices, such as flags or a sign, to make sure that visitors are unwelcome unless invited. Create a password for your friends.

Setting up camp

The whole idea of a camp is to put it somewhere where you won't be disturbed, and bring plenty of rations with you to keep you going. The beauty of this tent is that you can fold it up, store it, and use it again and again.

For the camp you will need
- 12 bamboo canes
- Strong tape and scissors
- An old blanket or rug
- Clothes pegs

Tape the sticks together

Lay out the bamboo canes in the position shown and tape each corner and the centre securely.

1.5 m (5 ft)

1.2 m (4 ft)

1.8 m (6 ft)

1.8 m (6 ft)

1.2 m (4 ft)

1.5 m (5 ft)

You will need two of these frames for the hideout.

Wrap the tape round and round to make sure the frame is secure.

Complete your hideaway

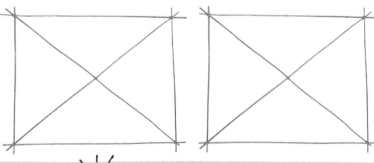

Make 2 of these

You will need a friend to help you hold them up.

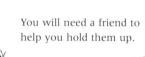

Stand the two frames up in a triangle shape and tape the two top ends together tightly.

Make sure you make the hideout wide enough to fit inside.

Bamboo canes

Bamboo canes

4 canes at 1.2 m (4 ft)

4 canes at 1.5 m (5 ft)

4 canes at 1.8 m (6 ft)

Bamboo canes

You will need 12 bamboo canes to make your hideout. If you need to cut them, ask an adult to help you.

Fly the flag

- 1 bamboo cane
- A piece of scrap material
- String

Paint a design on your flag and snip down the edges to make a zig-zag pattern. Then bunch up two corners and tie them to the pole with string.

Picnic bowl

- 3 x 60 cm (2 ft) bamboo canes
- Strong tape, plastic bowl

Tie the three poles together in the centre, let them go, and pop a plastic bowl on top. Fill with rations.

Tie the poles tightly in the middle.

When you let go of the poles they should fall into a stool shape and balance perfectly on three legs.

Drape the rug or blanket over the top of the framework.

Password please!

Make a "no entry" sign out of cardboard for privacy.

Use clothes pegs to attach the rug to the frame at the bottom.

59

Picnic in a pot
Look, no left-overs!

Edible pots

Anything delicious can be put into an ice cream cone – sweet or savoury snacks. Perfect for picnics, no mess to clear up!

popcorn

Surprise pots

Spoon delicious dips into
the bottom of your pots
and put fruit or
vegetables on top.

cream cheese dip

yogurt or cream

Taramasalata

Mayonnaise

61

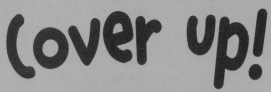

(over up!

Wear your art on your clothes,
and keep the sun off too!

GraffiT-shirt
Make your mark

Fabric pens are the easiest way to decorate a
T-shirt. Draw your design straight on, then
iron it to make it permanent.

Remember to put
paper or card inside
the T-shirt to stop the
ink going through.

You will need:
- White or light-coloured cotton T-shirt
- Fabric pens

T-shirts

White and pale-coloured T-shirts work best when decorating or dying. If you use a dark T-shirt the decoration won't show as clearly. So get out your old T-shirts and cover up!

Transform your clothes

Crazy faces

You could use any material to decorate your hats and bags, but felt is a great one to use. It is easy to cut and can be stuck onto other material easily using PVA or fabric glue.

Practise your face shapes on newspaper first. Then cut them out.

Use the paper templates to draw on to the fabric.

Cut out the shapes.

what to do

• Practise your shapes on a piece of newspaper.
• Use your newspaper template to cut out the felt shapes.
• Glue them into position.

Glue the shapes.

PVA glue

You will need:

• Scraps of fabric, such as felt
• Newspaper
• Scissors
• PVA or fabric glue

Stick into position.

Tie-dye T-shirts

The secret of tie-dye is the elastic bands. By tying them tightly the dye will not colour the tied bits, leaving swirls of pattern. When you are dying fabrics, make sure you read and follow the instructions on the dye packet.

⭐ **Ask an adult** to help with hot water.

Tie the bands

Scrunch up pieces of your T-shirt and tie elastic bands tightly to each little scrunch.

Follow the guidelines on the packet.

Mix up the dye

Now dunk your T-shirt into the dye and leave for however long the instructions tell you. Use rubber gloves.

Dunk in a T-shirt

Take it out and rinse it

Remove the bands

Rinse the T-shirt until the colour stops running out. Remove the elastic bands to reveal the twisty, swirly pattern. Then hang it up in the sun to dry.

Remember to use a light T-shirt otherwise the dye won't show.

The more elastic bands you use, the more patterns you get.

Thirst aid

Instant lemon soothies

to be taken in emergencies.

Lemon remedy contains:

 +  +  =

3 MEDIUM LEMONS   I LITRE WATER   SUGAR

Now sit back and take it squeezy!

Fizzy lemonade

For extra fizz, dilute your lemonade with fizzy mineral water.

Lemon popsicles

66

Lemon twister

A sugary candy twist with a slice of lemon in the middle makes a perfect stirrer.

Lemon take-away

Re-use empty drinks bottles and fill them up with a batch of home-made lemonade.

Crusty, sugary rim

Long cool lemon

Fill a tall glass with lots of ice and let it melt away into your lemonade.

Ice cube lemonpops

ways to add sweetness

• Use candy canes and lollypops as stirrers.

• For a yummy, sugary crust on the rim of the glass, tip out some sugar on to a plate. Hold a glass upside down and dip the rim into water then into the sugar. Leave it to dry.

Thirst aid kit

This lemonade recipe will make just over one litre. It may be tangy so add sugar or extra water until it tastes good. The best thing to do is experiment.

Remember to save some to make ice lollies and ice cubes.

Drink up

Your lemonade will only keep for two days in the fridge. So make sure you drink it quickly!

Squeeze to meet you

THE THIRST AID KIT

CHOPPING BOARD

FUNNEL

LARGE SPOON

SHARP KNIFE

BLENDER

LARGE JUG OR BOWL

MEASURING JUG

SIEVE

Making lemonade

Scrub all the lemons well as you will be using the whole fruit – even the peel!

- 3 lemons
- 1 litre water
- Sugar to taste

⭐ **Ask an adult** to help with the blender.

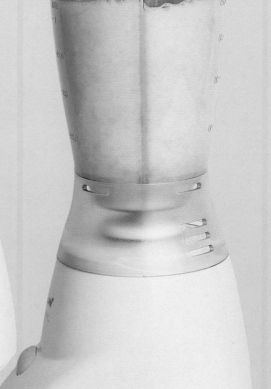

1 Wash the lemons and chop each into eight pieces.

2 Put the lemons into a blender and add some of the water.

3 Blend until the mixture is smooth.

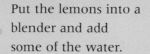

ice cube lollies

Place some fruit lollies into an ice cube tray and simply top up with your lemonade. Put them into the freezer over night and you have ice-cold, fruity lemonade lollipops!

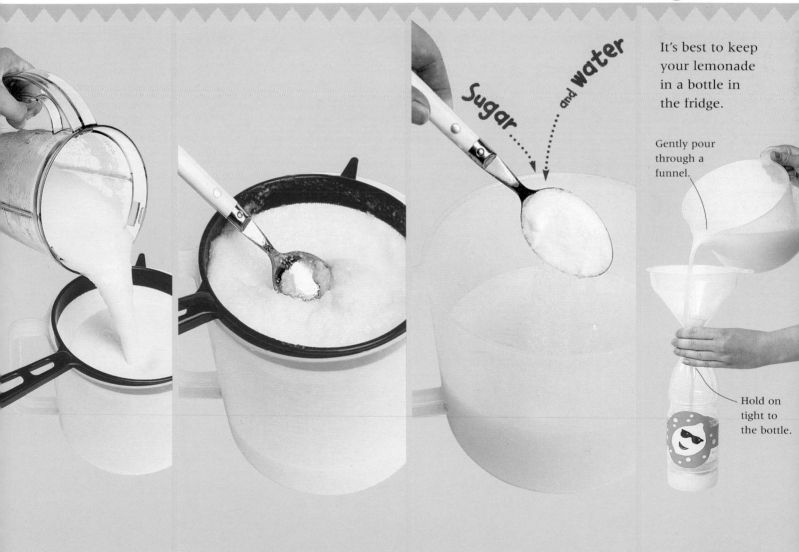

It's best to keep your lemonade in a bottle in the fridge.

Sugar and **water**

Gently pour through a funnel.

Hold on tight to the bottle.

4 Pour the mixture into a sieve.

5 Let the juice drain through, by pressing it with the back of a spoon.

6 Add some sugar to taste and the remaining water.

7 Bottle your lemonade.

Bowls of ice

Ice bowl tips

• To remove your ice bowl, leave it out at room temperature for a while to loosen it.

• Put the ice bowl back into the freezer for a few minutes to cool it again.

• Remember the bowl will melt in the hot sun so eat up!

70

Freeze an ice bowl

keep your food and drinks cool in a chilly ice bowl. You could use other fruit around the edges or even flowers and leaves.

1. Place a smaller bowl inside a larger one. Cut two lemons into thin slices and position them in the gap between the bowls.

2. Fill the gap with water. Place a stone in the centre of the small bowl and tape it securely to the larger bowl to hold it in place.

3. Put it into the freezer overnight. When you take it out, leave it out and let it melt slightly. Gently remove the bowls to reveal your ice bowl!

Fill your bowl with fruit. Quick – eat it up before it melts!

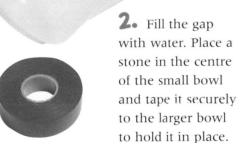

Don't lose your cool

The BIG freeze

Hello, ice to meet you!

Keep ultra cool on a hot, sunny day.
Create icy shapes and turn them ice blue.

Blue cubes

For blue ice cubes, add food colouring to the water before you fill up the tray.

Sugar-coated cooler

Dip the top rim of a glass in some water.

Now dip the rim in a dish of sugar.

The sugar will stick to the glass.

Fill with lemonade and drop in the ice cubes. Look how it turns blue – how refreshing!

Ice sculpture cocktail

Not just cubes – water will freeze into any shape you like. Try a balloon, the bottom of a plastic bottle, or even a rubber glove for some really spooky frozen fingers!

Add food colouring to the water before you freeze it to make coloured ice

Ice tips

• For hand and balloon shapes, make sure you seal the water by tying up the balloon or using a clothes peg on the rubber glove. You may have to cut the balloon and the glove to release them, so make sure you use an old glove.

• Run the shapes under cold water if they are difficult to take out of their moulds.

Rubber glove

Frozen fingers

Balloon

Rain cloud

Jelly mould

Snowball

Floating flower

Plastic bottle base

Iceberg

Plastic bag

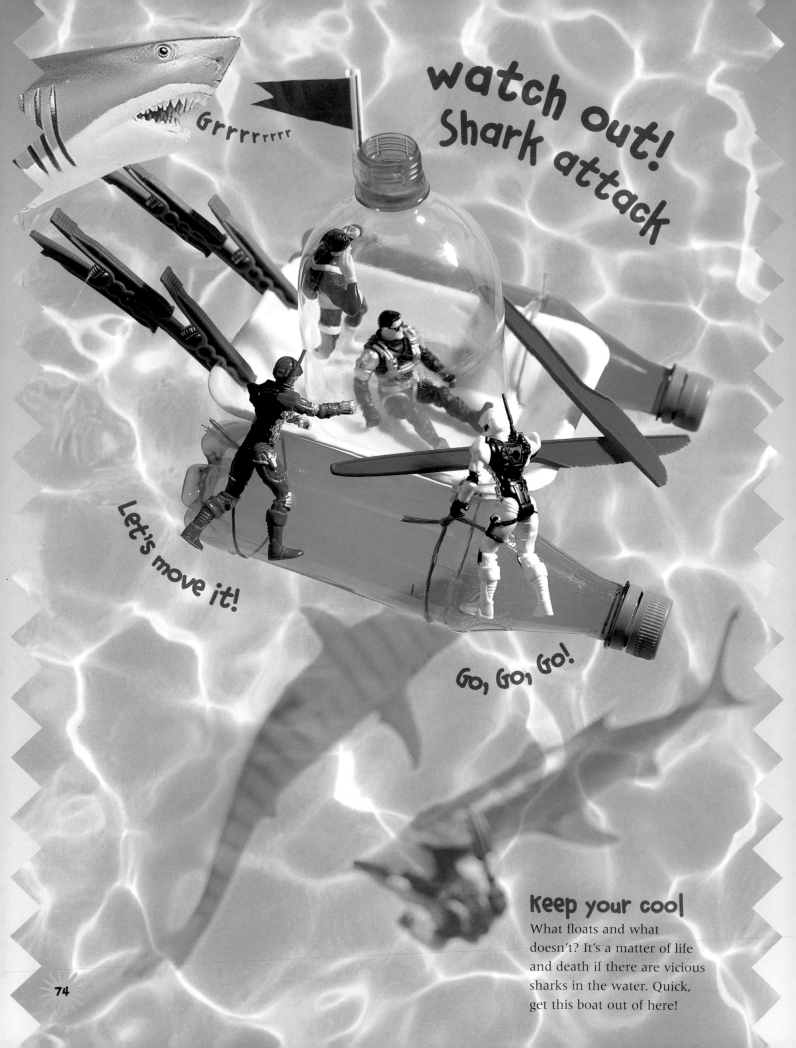

watch out! Shark attack

Grrrrrrrr

Let's move it!

Go, Go, Go!

keep your cool

What floats and what doesn't? It's a matter of life and death if there are vicious sharks in the water. Quick, get this boat out of here!

Crafty boats

Think or you'll sink! All you need to remember is, if it floats it'll make a boat. You'll need it to float if the sharks are about!

use anything you can find that floats for boat-building materials

To make a basic boat

All you need are two plastic bottles and a plastic food tray. When you have finished, add special features, such as a control deck or a go-faster spoiler.

Carefully make a hole in each corner.

Plastic bottle   Plastic food tray   Plastic bottle

Scissors and string

Tie a piece of string through each hole and around each bottle tightly.

★ **Ask an adult** to help when you are near water.

Fluttering **flags** and bunting to liven up *your sunny day party.*

Bags of **flags**

Transform plastic carrier bags into festive banners that flutter in the breeze.

Start collecting colourful plastic bags

Bags of fun

Every time someone goes shopping in your family, keep the plastic bags. You'll be amazed how useful they can be!

How to make flags from bags

Bags of bunting

All you have to do is make a template in a triangle shape. Cut the triangles out of plastic bags and attach them with string. Have bags of fun!

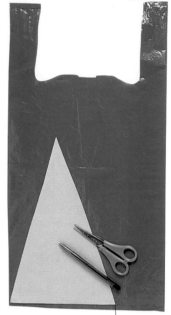

Cut out a paper triangle template.

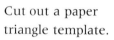

Draw a line around the paper.

Cut out lots and lots of colourful triangles.

Bags of flags

Cut a plastic drinks bottle into bands to make the flag support to tape strips of plastic to. Perfect to hang up in a breezy place to flutter in the wind.

⭐ **Ask an adult** to help cut the bottle.

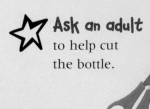

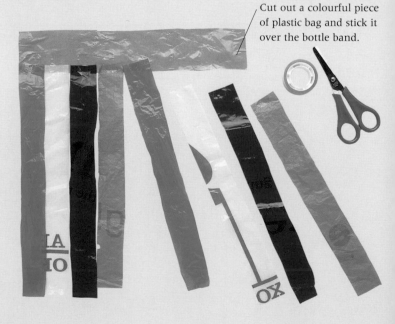

Cut out a colourful piece of plastic bag and stick it over the bottle band.

Cut the bottle into 5 cm (2 in) bands.

Cut strips of plastic and tape them to the plastic band.

use all sorts of plastic bags to make trillions of triangles

Lay the triangles in a row and place a long piece of string along the bottom.

Tape the string in place.

Fold the plastic over the string and staple it in place.

Wrap the band into a circular shape and attach the ends with tape.

Attach some string to the band and hang it up outside.

79

Streamers on parade

You will need:

• A drinking cup • Garden cane • Plastic bag • Scissors • Glue • Sticky tape

Cut out the base of a cup.

Make two holes in the side for the cane.

Use a sharp pencil to make the holes.

Push the cane through the holes.

Glue the cane in place and add some sticky tack for decoration.

Bring the folded bag up through the bottom of the cup.

Fold the bag so that it is a strip about 4 cm (2 in) wide.

Bring the bag over the cane and tape it in place.

Add some decoration.

Starting from the bottom, cut the bag into strips about 2 cm (1 in) wide to the base of the cup.

Streaming by

By running and running with the streamers in the sunshine, you will make a whooshing sound behind you. When you have finished running, plant them in the ground and let them wave in the breeze.

watch us race with

swishing streamers

Party time!

81

Sun catchers

Shimmering, glittering mobiles
twist and turn in the breeze catching the bright sunlight.

Silver scraps

Look out for things lying around the house that reflect the sun. Try CDs, gift wrap, and shiny plastic bottles.

How to catch the sun

Jazz up your garden by finding anything that shines, glitters, or shimmers, and make mobiles with it. As they twist and turn in the sunlight they glisten and dance. And on a dull day they will simply cheer up the garden.

Spiral catcher

The basic shape of this sun catcher is a spiral of kitchen foil and a used CD. However with a bit of imagination you can turn it into a real dazzler. Add sequins, shiny buttons, old Christmas decorations, or even double- up the spiral to make an enormous spiral catcher!

String

Twisted foil

CD

1. Cut about a 60 cm (2 ft) length of kitchen foil.

2. Scrunch and twist it up in your hands until it is a solid tube.

3. Twist it around your hand. Add another for a longer spiral.

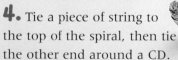

4. Tie a piece of string to the top of the spiral, then tie the other end around a CD.

Leave some extra string at the top to hang it up.

Decide where you want the CD to hang before you tie it.

Dancing paper plates

The secret to the paper plate catcher is to decorate both sides of the plate, that way whichever way it turns it will sparkle.

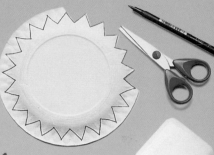

1. Draw a zig-zag around a paper plate and cut it out.

Shiny sweet wrappers

2. Now cover it with lots of shiny things.

Foil dish

Sequins

3. Tape some string to the back and add any other shiny things you can find.

Christmas bauble

84

Bottle-bell mobile

- Take a piece of card – 3 cm (1 in) across – poke a hole through the middle of it, and thread it half way along a piece of string. Fix it in place.
- Thread a button below it.
- Now attach some decorations such as CDs, baubles, and anything else that shimmers.
- Now simply thread the bottle-bell through the top of the string and it will sit on the card.

Piece of card

Button

String

CD

Bauble

How to make the bottle-bell

1. Cut the bottom off a drinks bottle.

2. Cut 2 cm (^{1}/2 in) strips about two-thirds of the way up the bottle.

3. Roll each strip up with your fingers and they will curl.

These old, shiny decorations are perfect. Squeeze two together and they will stay attached!

Let's sparkle in the sunlight

4. Thread the string through the neck of the bottle.

Thread it through until it sits on the card.

85

Tiny camps for tiny toys

A camp within a camp. On the edge of your garden camp sits another tiny adventure world. Let's get building!

This way for the building site

Portable campsite

Camps on trays are very useful as you can take them inside if it rains. You could use anything to decorate your landscape, you could even lay a little soil and plant some small flowers in it. Work out what you would like best in a campsite and get building!

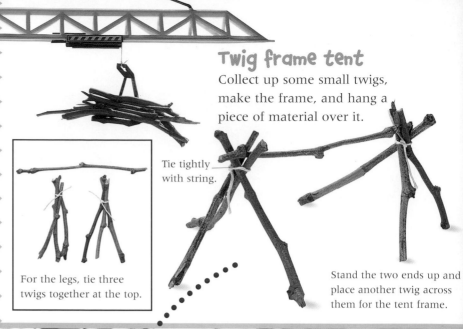

Twig frame tent

Collect up some small twigs, make the frame, and hang a piece of material over it.

Tie tightly with string.

For the legs, tie three twigs together at the top.

Stand the two ends up and place another twig across them for the tent frame.

Tiny Swing

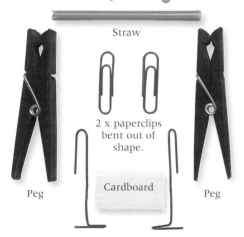

Straw

2 x paperclips bent out of shape.

Cardboard

Peg

Peg

Tape the paperclips to the cardboard to make the seat. Then hook them over the straw.

Baby bunting

Collect some pieces of coloured paper and a long piece of string.

Cut the paper into diamond shapes.

Glue one side of the diamond.

Fold it over the string with the glue on the inside to form a triangle.

Get camping!

Put it together! Take a tray and fill it will sand, gravel, or soil. Find some pebbles or rocks and place them around the edge. Now use your imagination to fill it with teeny, tiny camping gear.

I can't wait to move in!

Pebbles create a good landscape.

Use pebbles to keep the material down

A tiny picnic stand made with three twigs and a bottle top.

Sponge fish

A pond made out of a food container.

You could use sand as your base

Casting Shadows

View the world from some strange angles using shadows from the sun, and then capture them on camera.

Snap happy! Don't be camera sh

You will need:

- A camera – disposable cameras are handy
- Some willing models
- Your imagination
- Lots of bright sunshine

Call me Turkey!

Special effects

Hand shadows against a wall are great, but why not use your whole body to create some really strange shadow effects. You could even base a story around your shadow photos.

Fun in the Sun – what can we play?

Make a water bomb

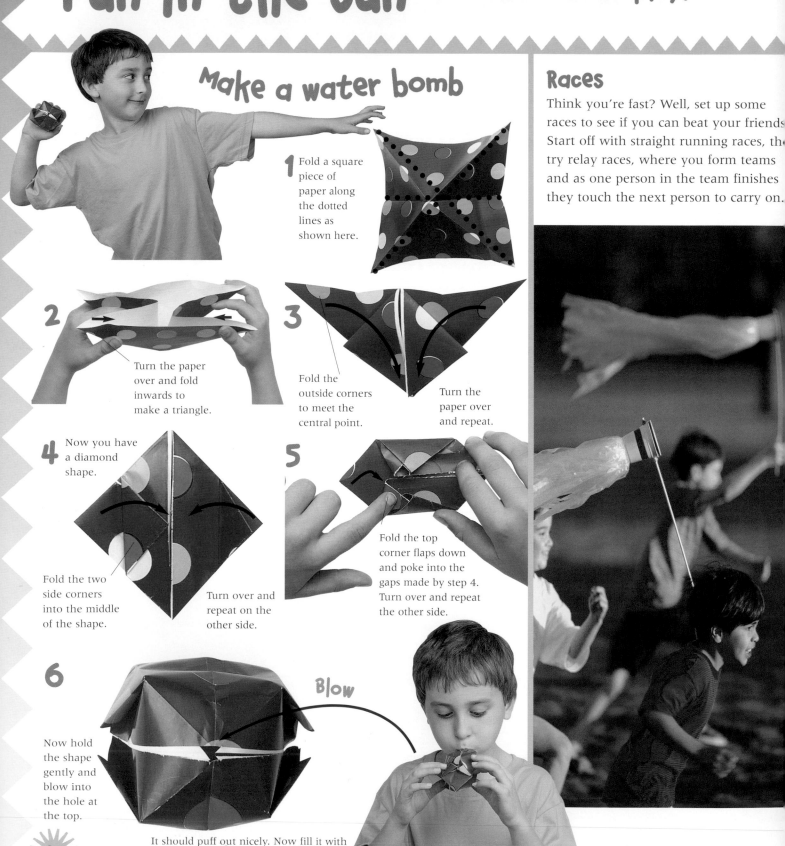

1 Fold a square piece of paper along the dotted lines as shown here.

2 Turn the paper over and fold inwards to make a triangle.

3 Fold the outside corners to meet the central point. Turn the paper over and repeat.

4 Now you have a diamond shape.

Fold the two side corners into the middle of the shape. Turn over and repeat on the other side.

5 Fold the top corner flaps down and poke into the gaps made by step 4. Turn over and repeat the other side.

6 Now hold the shape gently and blow into the hole at the top.

Blow

It should puff out nicely. Now fill it with water through the hole and throw!

Races

Think you're fast? Well, set up some races to see if you can beat your friends. Start off with straight running races, then try relay races, where you form teams and as one person in the team finishes they touch the next person to carry on.

Games with paper, games with balls, games with water, fun in the sun.

Drink on the go....

No cup handy? Here's a quick way to make one out of a piece of square paper.

1 Fold a square piece of paper in half to make a triangle shape.

2 Fold the corner of the triangle up as shown here.

3 Repeat with the other corner.

4 Fold down the top. Turn over and repeat on the other side.

Slurp!

Shadow tag

Instead of touching each other, as in a game of tag, try jumping on each other's shadow. The person chasing has to try to stand on someone's shadow, when they do that person becomes the chaser. You won't find it easy!

You can't catch me!

Here, catch the ball

Obstacle course

Ask an adult for some bits and bobs from around the garden or house that you can use to set up an obstacle course in the garden. Then time each other to finish it.

Jump over the broom, hop on one leg through the tyres, and kick the ball!

Football skills

The garden is the best place to brush up on your football skills – you are less likely to cause any damage! How many times can you keep the ball up using your knees?

93

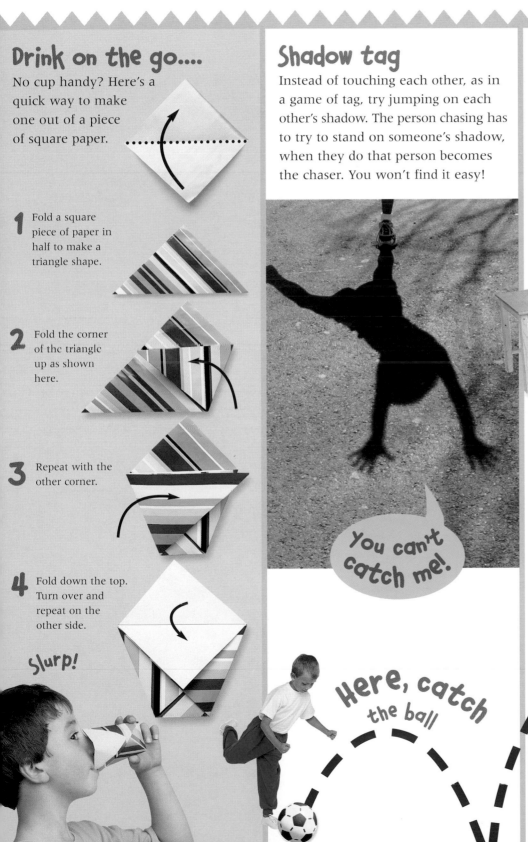

Ready, steady, GO! Get out into the sunshine – play some games,

Blowing bubbles

Make your own bubble mixture, then search your house for things that you think you could blow bubbles through. You can make lots and lots of tiny bubbles or huge giant ones.

Mix the recipe in a big bowl

what makes a good bubble?

Bend wire or old coathangers into shapes to make you own blowers.

Gently **blow** through the gaps.

Bubble recipe
Use one large cup of washing-up liquid, then mix in two large jugs of water.

Boing

94

then more games, and when you have finished, play even more!

water squirters

One of the most refreshing ways to cool off in the hot sun is to get completely soaked. So get into your swimming clothes and if you don't have a water squirter, then try making one. Plastic bottles are good, but try old shampoo or washing up liquid bottles too. It's all a matter of experimenting.

Ball games

Any ball games are fun. If you have a lot of friends with you then split into teams and compete against each other. Choose a team captain and make sure you agree about the rules before you start. If you want to play football, set up goal posts using bits and pieces found around your garden.

☆ **Ask an adult** to watch you when you are around water.

Here, catch the ball

Hide and seek

Ask a friend to count to 50 and find the best hiding place you can in the garden. Keep very still and very quiet and wait until the seeker finds you. The first to be found is the seeker next time round. Sometimes the best hiding places are the most obvious ones. Remember, keep still!

. . . and hide-aways

A secret camp in the garden is a great way to keep out of the sun and to form a club. For an instant and temporary camp, try using chairs with a blanket draped over them and one on the floor. Fill it with cushions.

Happy sunny days!

INDEX

Did you spot Bob?

Look for him on pages:
4, 17, 24, 39, 42, 44, and 46.

ACKNOWLEDGEMENTS

With thanks to the models . . .
Maisie Armah, Eleanor Bates, Luke
Bower, Charlotte, Billy, and James
Bull, Seriye Ezigwe, Max, Guy, and
Imogen Lowery, and Sorcha Lyons for
being fantastic everyday models

The publishers would like to thank the
following for their kind permission to
reproduce their photographs: (Abbreviations
key: t=top, b=bottom, r=right, c=centre)

43tl Stuart McClymont, 43tr Corbis: Richard
Ransier;, 43bl Getty Images: Robert Stahl;
44r Corbis: Peter N. Fox; 45c Getty Images:
Robert Stahl; 46r Corbis: Peter Steiner; 47l
Corbis: Dirk Douglass.

All other images © Dorling Kindersley.
For further information see:
www.dkimages.com

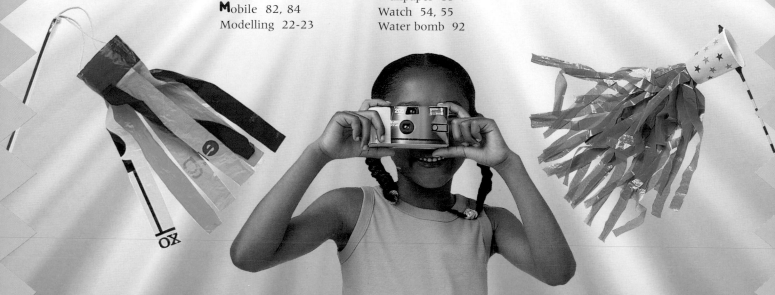